AMBER
the Boxer Dog

Story by
Clara Barnes Link

Photography by
R. Edward Link

Acknowledgments

This book is dedicated to my husband, Eddie,
for always believing in me and telling me to try.
Special thanks goes to my writing teacher, Maureen Ryan Griffin,
whose continued guidance and encouragement has helped me
make this book a reality and a dream come true.
Clara Barnes Link
Lake Norman, North Carolina
2017

FLOATING LEAF PRESS
A division of
WordPlay
Email: info@wordplaynow.com
www.wordplaynow.com

Library of Congress Control Number 2017947263

ISBN 978-0-9802304-4-4

For Everly

…learning to say, "Yes, I can," *instead of*
"No, I can't."

—Julia Cameron,
from *Finding Water*

My name is Amber and I am a boxer dog.
Sometimes people point at me and say, "Look, a bulldog."

But I am NOT a bulldog. I am a boxer dog.

Even though I have a serious face with a flat nose,
and some people might think I'm a little scary,
I am a very friendly and gentle dog.

Sometimes I do funny things to make people laugh.
But I do some pretty amazing things, too,
just because I decided to try.
To explain how this happened,
we have to start back at the beginning of my story.

I was born on a farm in Tennessee. This is my mother. She told me many times in those first few weeks of my life that I could learn to do whatever I set my mind to. But I was a puppy and did not understand what she meant.

One day a man came to my farm. Out of all
my brothers and sisters, he picked me to go and
live with him. We rode a long way to his house.
I heard him say it was three hundred miles.

On the way, he told me about my new family. The man
had a wife, three daughters, and one son. They lived
in a gray house with a big yard, and best of all,
the man said there was a lake beside their house.

When the man and I arrived at his house,
I met my new family. Here's a picture
of me and the oldest daughter, Jennifer.
She could tell I was a little afraid of this new place,
and gave me a kiss to comfort me.

This is a picture of me and the son, Raymond.
I felt safe on his lap. Raymond, Jennifer,
Holly, and Mary Mae (the other two daughters),
all thought I was cute and immediately
loved me, just like the man did. So did the mom.

At night when the family was together, I would listen
from my little bed as the man talked to the children.
He told them that when they were asked to try new things,
he didn't want them to say "No, I can't," but to just try.

I remembered what my mother said, that I could learn
to do whatever I wanted if I set my mind to it.
I decided I would try, too.

First, I tried floating with the man in the water.
It was fun to stand on the man's belly
while we drifted around the lake.

As I grew, I tried jumping off the pier into the lake.

Then, I swam back and climbed the ladder. It was tiring, but fun, so after resting, I did it again and again.

Next I tried distance swimming, complete with goggles
and a life jacket. I found out I was good at it,
on account of my strong legs.
What else could I be good at?

The man was good at catching fish
from the lake and I liked to watch them
flip flop on the pier. I didn't want
to catch fish. But I did want to do
something important the way he did.

When I watched the man cut the grass, it looked like fun.
And I knew it was important, because he did it a lot.
I asked him if I could try.

He said, "Sure!"

I only needed him to start the mower for me
and I took care of the rest.

The mom was good at sewing. She made beautiful, useful things.
This was important work, too.

I wanted to help her and she said, "Of course."

She taught me to use the sewing machine
and we made pretty dresses for the daughters.

The youngest daughter, Mary Mae, told me that wearing glasses makes you look smart. What do you think?

This gave me an idea. I decided I wanted to go to school.

The man explained that dogs were not allowed at school.

But he had another idea.
I could do my schooling at home.
There were lots of books to learn from.
Mary Mae showed me where to start.

I took online courses, too. I wore a headset
so I wouldn't disturb the family.

Many nights, I stayed up late,
reading and studying in bed.

I went to sleep tired.

Finally, the day came when I graduated
and received my diploma.

Here is a picture of me as all three sisters,
Jennifer, Mary Mae, and Holly, congratulated me
on my educational accomplishment.
(I use big words like this now that I have graduated.)
The whole family was very proud of me.

In fact, the man was so proud of me
that he gave me my own car, a convertible
that I can drive around with the top down.
He also bought me a leather coat so I won't get cold.

After my schooling was finished, I decided to get a job. First,
I worked at the ice cream shop, since I can scoop out ice cream fast.

Now I drive the truck for a tree service,
because I'm good at that, too.

Sometimes, if they're short-handed, I operate the forklift.

But don't think my life is all work and no play.
The man and I like to swing on our rope swing together.

I also like riding on the coin-operated boat
outside the coffee shop in town.

Other times, I relax with the man, enjoying the view
as he points out the names of the nearby mountains.

And lately, I've been hanging out with Everly, the newest member of the family. She reminds me of my puppy days when I was small and starting to learn so many new things.

The family always includes me on vacations.
One of my favorite places to go is the beach.
Jumping the waves as they roll in is fun.

Jumping on the beach is fun, too.
Raymond and I love to play
with sticks together.

I chill out in my chair
and listen to music…

I even let the children bury me in the sand.
I don't know why…

At sunset, when there are a few quiet moments,
I remember again the words of my mother:
"You can learn to do whatever you set your mind to."

Don't say, "I can't." Take it from me.
Instead, say, "I can."

About the Author

Clara Barnes Link has lived on Lake Norman for over thirty years with her husband, Eddie. They have raised four children, along with several dogs, cats, fish, and one lone gerbil.

This is Clara's first children's book, based on a very special member of their family – Amber, or as her husband sometimes calls her, "Ambrosia."

About the Photographer

R. Edward (Eddie) Link uses photography to record the humorous events and activities of everyday life at his place on Lake Norman, especially those of his children and family pets.

51996604R00028

Made in the USA
San Bernardino, CA
08 August 2017